A Cup

of

Faith

Interior images used under license from Shutterstock.com

Castle Point Publishing
58 Ninth Street
Hoboken, NJ 07030

www.castlepointpub.com

ISBN: 978-0-9982297-0-6

Printed and bound in the United States of America

10 9 8 7 6 5 4 3

HOW TO USE THIS JOURNAL

Finding time for God is a priority for many of us, but sometimes we need a little help to fit it into our busy life. This journal, and the comfort it brings, is as essential to a wonderful day as a warm cup of coffee or tea. Use the prompts in the pages that follow to carry on a meaningful conversation with God and build on your understanding of your faith and yourself.

Begin each day right by jotting down a favorite piece of scripture or one that you'd like to consider more deeply. Allow the playful artwork that decorates each page to spark your creativity as you go on to read the day's prompts. Follow your inspiration as you begin to write your innermost thoughts and feelings on the blank spaces provided and open your heart to God.

Use *A Cup of Faith* to deepen your devotion and turn small moments of free time into an opportunity for meaningful reflection. Share your prayers and your hopes with the Lord as you write them on the pages that follow. With *A Cup of Faith* to guide you on a thought-provoking journey, you'll enjoy the peace and comfort that comes from spending more quality time with God.

DATE _____

TODAY'S SCRIPTURE READING:

_____
_____
_____

Today I feel God's love through...

_____
_____
_____
_____
_____
_____
_____
_____
_____

Faith means...

_____
_____
_____
_____
_____
_____
_____
_____

A small miracle I have witnessed is...

_____
_____
_____
_____
_____
_____
_____
_____
_____

God, help me today with...

_____
_____
_____
_____
_____
_____
_____
_____

DATE _____

TODAY'S SCRIPTURE READING:

_____
_____
_____

My prayer to God is...

_____
_____
_____
_____
_____
_____
_____

My family is a blessing because...

_____
_____
_____
_____
_____
_____
_____
_____

Today I am thankful for...

_____
_____
_____
_____
_____
_____
_____
_____

In my heart today...

_____
_____
_____
_____
_____
_____
_____

DATE _____

TODAY'S SCRIPTURE READING:

_____
_____
_____

I thank God for...

_____
_____
_____
_____
_____
_____
_____

Today I am hoping for...

_____
_____
_____
_____
_____
_____
_____
_____
_____

My life is wonderful today because...

_____
_____
_____
_____
_____
_____
_____
_____

Today I am grateful that God gave me...

_____
_____
_____
_____
_____
_____
_____
_____
_____

DATE _____

TODAY'S SCRIPTURE READING:

_____
_____
_____

I need to trust God with...

I feel God's presence when...

_____
_____
_____
_____
_____
_____
_____
_____
_____
_____

_____
_____
_____
_____
_____
_____
_____

My faith in God has taught me...

_____
_____
Through God I am working
to forgive...

_____
_____
_____
_____
_____
_____
_____
_____
_____
_____
_____
_____
_____
_____
_____
_____
_____

DATE _____

TODAY'S SCRIPTURE READING:

_____
_____
_____

Today I feel blessed because...

_____
_____
_____
_____
_____
_____
_____
_____
_____

Through God I work to better understand people who...

_____
_____
_____
_____
_____
_____
_____
_____
_____

I will live God's plan for me by...

_____
_____
_____
_____
_____
_____
_____
_____
_____

Something that brings me joy is...

_____
_____
_____
_____
_____
_____
_____
_____
_____

DATE _____

I am joyful today because...

TODAY'S SCRIPTURE READING:

_____

_____
_____
_____
_____

Today I ask God for...

_____
_____
_____

I feel surrounded by God's
love when...

_____
_____
_____
_____
_____
_____
_____
_____

I will surrender to God today by...

_____
_____
_____
_____
_____
_____
_____

DATE _____

TODAY'S SCRIPTURE READING:

_____
_____
_____

Lord, teach me to...

_____
_____
_____
_____
_____
_____
_____
_____

With God's love I can...

_____
_____
_____
_____
_____
_____
_____
_____
_____
_____
_____

God loves me despite...

_____
_____
_____
_____
_____
_____
_____
_____
_____

Today I saw God.....

_____
_____
_____
_____
_____
_____
_____
_____

DATE _____

TODAY'S SCRIPTURE READING:

_____
_____
_____

Faith means...

_____
_____
_____
_____
_____
_____
_____

Today I feel God's love through...

_____
_____
_____
_____
_____
_____
_____
_____
_____

God, help me today with...

_____
_____
_____
_____
_____
_____

A small miracle I have
witnessed is...

_____
_____
_____
_____
_____
_____

DATE _____

TODAY'S SCRIPTURE READING:

_____
_____
_____

Today I am thankful for...

My prayer to God is...

_____
_____
_____
_____
_____
_____
_____
_____
_____
_____
_____
_____
_____
_____
_____
_____
_____

In my heart today...

My family is a blessing because...

_____
_____
_____
_____
_____
_____
_____
_____
_____
_____
_____
_____
_____
_____
_____
_____

DATE _____

TODAY'S SCRIPTURE READING:

_____
_____
_____

I thank God for...

_____
_____
_____
_____
_____
_____
_____

Today I am hoping for...

_____
_____
_____
_____
_____
_____
_____

My life is wonderful
today because...

_____
_____
_____
_____
_____
_____
_____
_____

Today I am grateful that God
gave me...

_____
_____
_____
_____
_____
_____

DATE _____

TODAY'S SCRIPTURE READING:

_____
_____
_____

I feel God's presence when...

_____
_____
_____
_____
_____
_____
_____
_____

Through God I am working
to forgive...

_____
_____
_____
_____
_____
_____
_____
_____

I need to trust God with...

_____
_____
_____
_____
_____
_____
_____
_____

My faith in God has taught me...

_____
_____
_____
_____
_____
_____
_____

DATE _____

TODAY'S SCRIPTURE READING:

_____
_____
_____

Through God I work to better understand people who...

Today I feel blessed because...

_____
_____
_____
_____
_____
_____
_____
_____
_____
_____

Something that brings me joy is...

I will live God's plan for me by...

_____
_____
_____
_____
_____
_____
_____

_____
_____
_____
_____
_____
_____

_____
_____
_____
_____
_____
_____
_____

DATE _____

TODAY'S SCRIPTURE READING:

_____
_____
_____

Today I ask God for...

_____
_____
_____
_____
_____
_____
_____
_____
_____

I am joyful today because...

_____
_____
_____
_____
_____

I feel surrounded by God's
love when...

_____
_____
_____
_____

I will surrender to God
today by...

_____
_____
_____
_____
_____
_____
_____
_____

_____
_____
_____
_____
_____
_____
_____
_____

DATE _____

God loves me despite...

_____
_____
_____

Lord, teach me to...

_____
_____
_____
_____
_____
_____
_____

Today I saw God.....

_____
_____
_____
_____
_____
_____
_____

With God's love I can...

_____
_____
_____
_____
_____
_____

DATE _____

TODAY'S SCRIPTURE READING:

_____
_____
_____

Today I feel God's love through...

_____
_____
_____
_____
_____
_____
_____
_____

Faith means...

_____
_____
_____
_____
_____
_____
_____
_____

A small miracle I have witnessed is...

_____
_____
_____
_____
_____
_____
_____
_____
_____

God, help me today with...

_____
_____
_____
_____
_____
_____
_____

DATE _____   Today I am thankful for...

TODAY'S SCRIPTURE READING: _____
_____   _____
_____   _____
_____   _____
                               _____
                               _____
My prayer to God is...   _____
                               _____
_____   _____
_____
_____   In my heart today...
_____
_____   _____
_____   _____
_____   _____
_____   _____
_____   _____
                               _____
My family is a blessing because...   _____
                               _____
_____   _____
_____   _____
_____
_____
_____
_____
_____
_____
_____

DATE _____

My life is wonderful today because...

TODAY'S SCRIPTURE READING:

_____
_____
_____

I thank God for...

_____
_____
_____
_____
_____
_____
_____
_____

_____
_____
_____
_____
_____
_____
_____

Today I am grateful that God gave me...

_____
_____
_____
_____
_____
_____
_____

Today I am hoping for...

_____
_____
_____
_____
_____
_____
_____
_____
_____
_____

DATE _____

TODAY'S SCRIPTURE READING:

_____
_____
_____

I need to trust God with...

I feel God's presence when...

_____
_____
_____
_____
_____
_____
_____
_____
_____
_____

_____
_____
_____
_____
_____
_____
_____

My faith in God has taught me...

Through God I am working
to forgive...

_____
_____
_____
_____
_____
_____
_____
_____

_____
_____
_____
_____
_____
_____
_____
_____
_____
_____
_____

DATE _____

TODAY'S SCRIPTURE READING:

_____
_____
_____

Today I feel blessed because...

_____
_____
_____
_____
_____
_____
_____
_____

Through God I work to better understand people who...

_____
_____
_____
_____
_____
_____
_____
_____

I will live God's plan for me by...

_____
_____
_____
_____
_____
_____
_____
_____

Something that brings me joy is...

_____
_____
_____
_____
_____
_____
_____

DATE _____

TODAY'S SCRIPTURE READING:

_____
_____
_____

Today I ask God for...

_____
_____
_____
_____
_____
_____
_____

I will surrender to God today by...

_____
_____
_____
_____
_____
_____
_____
_____

I am joyful today because...

_____
_____
_____
_____
_____
_____
_____
_____

I feel surrounded by God's love when...

_____
_____
_____
_____
_____
_____
_____

DATE _____

TODAY'S SCRIPTURE READING:

_____

_____

_____

Lord, teach me to...

_____

_____

_____

_____

_____

_____

_____

_____

With God's love I can...

_____

_____

_____

_____

_____

_____

_____

_____

_____

_____

_____

God loves me despite...

_____

_____

_____

_____

_____

_____

_____

_____

_____

_____

Today I saw God.....

_____

_____

_____

_____

_____

_____

_____

_____

_____

_____

_____

_____

DATE _____

TODAY'S SCRIPTURE READING:

_____
_____
_____

Faith means...

Today I feel God's love through...

_____
_____
_____
_____
_____
_____
_____
_____
_____

God, help me today with...

A small miracle I have
witnessed is...

_____
_____
_____
_____
_____
_____

DATE _____

TODAY'S SCRIPTURE READING:

_____
_____
_____

Today I am thankful for...

My prayer to God is...

_____
_____
_____
_____
_____
_____
_____
_____
_____

_____
_____
_____
_____
_____
_____
_____

In my heart today...

My family is a blessing because...

_____
_____
_____
_____
_____
_____
_____
_____
_____

_____
_____
_____
_____
_____
_____
_____
_____

DATE _____

TODAY'S SCRIPTURE READING:

_____
_____
_____

I thank God for...

_____
_____
_____
_____
_____
_____
_____

Today I am hoping for...

_____
_____
_____
_____
_____
_____
_____

My life is wonderful
today because...

_____
_____
_____
_____
_____
_____
_____
_____
_____

Today I am grateful that God
gave me...

_____
_____
_____
_____
_____
_____

DATE _____

TODAY'S SCRIPTURE READING:

_____
_____
_____

I feel God's presence when...

_____
_____
_____
_____
_____
_____
_____
_____

Through God I am working
to forgive...

_____
_____
_____
_____
_____
_____
_____
_____
_____

I need to trust God with...

_____
_____
_____
_____
_____
_____
_____
_____
_____

My faith in God has taught me...

_____
_____
_____
_____
_____
_____
_____
_____
_____

DATE _____

TODAY'S SCRIPTURE READING:

_____
_____
_____

Today I feel blessed because...

Through God I work to better understand people who...

_____
_____
_____
_____
_____
_____
_____
_____
_____

Something that brings me joy is...

I will live God's plan for me by...

_____
_____
_____
_____
_____
_____
_____
_____
_____

DATE _____

TODAY'S SCRIPTURE READING:

_____
_____
_____

Today I ask God for...

_____
_____
_____
_____
_____
_____
_____
_____

I am joyful today because...

_____
_____
_____
_____
_____

I feel surrounded by God's love when...

_____
_____
_____
_____
_____

I will surrender to God today by...

_____
_____
_____
_____
_____
_____
_____

_____
_____
_____
_____
_____
_____
_____

DATE _____

TODAY'S SCRIPTURE READING:

_____

_____

_____

Lord, teach me to...

_____

_____

_____

_____

_____

_____

_____

With God's love I can...

_____

_____

_____

_____

_____

_____

_____

God loves me despite...

_____

_____

_____

_____

_____

_____

_____

_____

_____

_____

Today I saw God.....

_____

_____

_____

_____

_____

_____

_____

DATE _____

TODAY'S SCRIPTURE READING:

_____
_____
_____

Today I feel God's love through...

Faith means...

_____
_____
_____
_____
_____
_____
_____
_____
_____

_____
_____
_____
_____
_____
_____
_____
_____
_____
_____

A small miracle I have witnessed is...

_____

God, help me today with...

_____
_____
_____
_____
_____
_____
_____
_____
_____

_____
_____
_____
_____
_____
_____
_____
_____

DATE _____   Today I am thankful for...

TODAY'S SCRIPTURE READING: _____

_____   _____

_____   _____

_____   _____

                                      _____

My prayer to God is...   _____

                                      _____

_____   _____

_____   _____

_____   In my heart today...

_____

_____   _____

_____   _____

_____   _____

_____   _____

                                      _____

My family is a blessing because...   _____

_____   _____

_____   _____

_____

_____

_____

_____

_____

_____

_____

DATE _____

TODAY'S SCRIPTURE READING:

_____
_____
_____

I thank God for...

_____
_____
_____
_____
_____
_____
_____

Today I am hoping for...

_____
_____
_____
_____
_____
_____
_____
_____
_____

My life is wonderful today because...

_____
_____
_____
_____
_____
_____
_____
_____

Today I am grateful that God gave me...

_____
_____
_____
_____
_____
_____
_____

DATE _____

TODAY'S SCRIPTURE READING:

_____
_____
_____

I need to trust God with...

I feel God's presence when...

_____
_____
_____
_____
_____
_____
_____
_____
_____
_____

_____
_____
_____
_____
_____
_____
_____

My faith in God has taught me...

_____
Through God I am working
to forgive...

_____
_____
_____
_____
_____
_____
_____

_____
_____
_____
_____
_____
_____
_____
_____
_____
_____

DATE _____

TODAY'S SCRIPTURE READING:

_____

_____

_____

Today I feel blessed because...

_____

_____

_____

_____

_____

_____

_____

_____

Through God I work to better understand people who...

_____

_____

_____

_____

_____

_____

_____

_____

_____

I will live God's plan for me by...

_____

_____

_____

_____

_____

_____

_____

_____

Something that brings me joy is...

_____

_____

_____

_____

_____

_____

_____

DATE _____

TODAY'S SCRIPTURE READING:

_____
_____
_____

Today I ask God for...

_____
_____
_____
_____
_____
_____
_____

I will surrender to God today by...

_____
_____
_____
_____
_____
_____
_____
_____
_____

I am joyful today because...

_____
_____
_____
_____
_____
_____
_____
_____
_____

I feel surrounded by God's
love when...

_____
_____
_____
_____
_____
_____
_____

DATE _____   God loves me despite...

TODAY'S SCRIPTURE READING: _____
_____   _____
_____   _____
_____   _____
_____   _____
                             _____
Lord, teach me to...   _____
                             _____
_____   _____
_____   _____
_____   _____
_____   Today I saw God.....
_____
_____   _____
_____   _____
_____   _____
                             _____
With God's love I can...   _____
                             _____
_____   _____
_____   _____
_____   _____
_____
_____
_____
_____
_____
_____
_____
_____

DATE _____

TODAY'S SCRIPTURE READING:

_____
_____
_____

Faith means...

Today I feel God's love through...

_____
_____
_____
_____
_____
_____
_____
_____
_____
_____
_____

_____
_____
_____
_____
_____
_____
_____
_____

God, help me today with...

A small miracle I have
witnessed is...

_____
_____
_____
_____
_____
_____

_____
_____
_____
_____
_____
_____
_____

DATE _____

TODAY'S SCRIPTURE READING:

_____
_____
_____

Today I am thankful for...

My prayer to God is...

_____
_____
_____
_____
_____
_____
_____
_____
_____

_____
_____
_____
_____
_____
_____
_____

In my heart today...

My family is a blessing because...

_____
_____
_____
_____
_____
_____
_____
_____
_____

_____
_____
_____
_____
_____
_____
_____
_____

DATE _____

TODAY'S SCRIPTURE READING:

_____
_____
_____

I thank God for...

_____
_____
_____
_____
_____
_____
_____
_____

Today I am hoping for...

_____
_____
_____
_____
_____
_____
_____

My life is wonderful
today because...

_____
_____
_____
_____
_____
_____
_____
_____

Today I am grateful that God
gave me...

_____
_____
_____
_____
_____
_____
_____
_____

DATE _____

TODAY'S SCRIPTURE READING:

_____

_____

_____

I feel God's presence when...

_____

_____

_____

_____

_____

_____

Through God I am working
to forgive...

_____

_____

_____

_____

_____

_____

_____

_____

I need to trust God with...

_____

_____

_____

_____

_____

_____

_____

_____

_____

My faith in God has taught me...

_____

_____

_____

_____

_____

_____

_____

_____

DATE _____

TODAY'S SCRIPTURE READING:

_____
_____
_____

Through God I work to better
understand people who...

Today I feel blessed because...

_____
_____
_____
_____
_____
_____
_____
_____
_____
_____
_____

_____
_____
_____
_____
_____
_____
_____

Something that brings me joy is...

I will live God's plan for me by...

_____
_____
_____
_____
_____
_____
_____
_____

_____
_____
_____
_____
_____
_____
_____
_____
_____

DATE _____

TODAY'S SCRIPTURE READING:

_____
_____
_____

Today I ask God for...

_____
_____
_____
_____
_____
_____
_____
_____

I am joyful today because...

_____
_____
_____
_____
_____

I feel surrounded by God's love when...

_____
_____
_____
_____

I will surrender to God today by...

_____
_____
_____
_____
_____
_____
_____
_____
_____
_____
_____

DATE _____   God loves me despite...

TODAY'S SCRIPTURE READING: _____
_____
_____
_____
_____

Lord, teach me to...   _____
_____
_____
_____
_____
_____
_____   Today I saw God.....
_____
_____
_____
_____
_____
_____
_____
_____
With God's love I can...   _____
_____
_____   _____
_____   _____
_____
_____
_____
_____
_____
_____
_____

DATE _____

TODAY'S SCRIPTURE READING:

_____
_____
_____

Today I feel God's love through...

_____
_____
_____
_____
_____
_____
_____
_____

Faith means...

_____
_____
_____
_____
_____
_____
_____
_____

A small miracle I have witnessed is...

_____
_____
_____
_____
_____
_____
_____

God, help me today with...

_____
_____
_____
_____
_____
_____
_____

DATE _____   Today I am thankful for...

TODAY'S SCRIPTURE READING:
_____
_____
_____
_____

My prayer to God is...
_____
_____
_____   In my heart today...
_____
_____
_____
_____
_____
_____

My family is a blessing because...
_____
_____
_____
_____
_____
_____
_____
_____
_____

DATE _____

TODAY'S SCRIPTURE READING:

_____
_____
_____

I thank God for...

_____
_____
_____
_____
_____
_____
_____

Today I am hoping for...

_____
_____
_____
_____
_____
_____
_____
_____
_____
_____

My life is wonderful today because...

_____
_____
_____
_____
_____
_____
_____
_____

Today I am grateful that God gave me...

_____
_____
_____
_____
_____
_____
_____
_____
_____

DATE _____

TODAY'S SCRIPTURE READING:

_____
_____
_____

I need to trust God with...

I feel God's presence when...

_____
_____
_____
_____
_____
_____
_____
_____
_____
_____

_____
_____
_____
_____
_____
_____
_____

My faith in God has taught me...

Through God I am working
to forgive...

_____
_____
_____
_____
_____
_____

_____
_____
_____
_____
_____
_____
_____
_____

DATE _____

TODAY'S SCRIPTURE READING:

_____
_____
_____

Today I feel blessed because...

_____
_____
_____
_____
_____
_____
_____
_____
_____

I will live God's plan for me by...

_____
_____
_____
_____
_____
_____
_____
_____
_____

Through God I work to better understand people who...

_____
_____
_____
_____
_____
_____
_____
_____
_____

Something that brings me joy is...

_____
_____
_____
_____
_____
_____
_____

DATE _____

TODAY'S SCRIPTURE READING:

_____
_____
_____

Today I ask God for...

_____
_____
_____
_____
_____
_____
_____

I will surrender to God today by...

_____
_____
_____
_____
_____
_____
_____
_____
_____

I am joyful today because...

_____
_____
_____
_____
_____
_____
_____
_____

I feel surrounded by God's
love when...

_____
_____
_____
_____
_____
_____
_____
_____

DATE _____   God loves me despite...

TODAY'S SCRIPTURE READING: _____
_____   _____
_____   _____
_____   _____
                                _____
                                _____
Lord, teach me to...   _____
                                _____
_____   _____
_____
_____
_____   Today I saw God.....
_____
_____   _____
_____   _____
_____   _____
                                _____
With God's love I can...   _____
                                _____
_____   _____
_____   _____
_____   _____
_____   _____
_____
_____
_____
_____
_____
_____
_____

DATE _____

TODAY'S SCRIPTURE READING:

_____
_____
_____

Faith means...

Today I feel God's love through...

_____
_____
_____
_____
_____
_____
_____
_____
_____
_____

God, help me today with...

A small miracle I have
witnessed is...

_____
_____
_____
_____
_____
_____

DATE _____

TODAY'S SCRIPTURE READING:

_____
_____
_____

Today I am thankful for...

My prayer to God is...

_____
_____
_____
_____
_____
_____
_____
_____
_____
_____

_____
_____
_____
_____
_____
_____
_____
_____

In my heart today...

My family is a blessing because...

_____
_____
_____
_____
_____
_____
_____
_____
_____
_____

_____
_____
_____
_____
_____
_____
_____
_____
_____

DATE _____

TODAY'S SCRIPTURE READING:

_____
_____
_____

I thank God for...

_____
_____
_____
_____
_____
_____
_____
_____

Today I am hoping for...

_____
_____
_____
_____
_____
_____
_____
_____

My life is wonderful
today because...

_____
_____
_____
_____
_____
_____
_____
_____
_____
_____

Today I am grateful that God
gave me...

_____
_____
_____
_____
_____
_____

DATE _____

TODAY'S SCRIPTURE READING:

_____
_____
_____

I feel God's presence when...

_____
_____
_____
_____
_____
_____
_____
_____

Through God I am working
to forgive...

_____
_____
_____
_____
_____
_____
_____
_____
_____
_____

I need to trust God with...

_____
_____
_____
_____
_____
_____
_____
_____
_____

My faith in God has taught me...

_____
_____
_____
_____
_____
_____
_____
_____

DATE _____

TODAY'S SCRIPTURE READING:

_____
_____
_____

Through God I work to better
understand people who...

Today I feel blessed because...

_____
_____
_____
_____
_____
_____
_____
_____
_____

_____
_____
_____
_____
_____
_____
_____

Something that brings me joy is...

I will live God's plan for me by...

_____
_____
_____
_____
_____
_____
_____
_____

_____
_____
_____
_____
_____
_____
_____
_____

DATE _____

TODAY'S SCRIPTURE READING:

_____
_____
_____

Today I ask God for...

_____
_____
_____
_____
_____
_____
_____
_____
_____

I will surrender to God
today by...

_____
_____
_____
_____
_____
_____
_____

I am joyful today because...

_____
_____
_____
_____
_____
_____

I feel surrounded by God's
love when...

_____
_____
_____
_____
_____
_____
_____
_____

DATE _____

TODAY'S SCRIPTURE READING:

_____

_____

_____

Lord, teach me to...

_____

_____

_____

_____

_____

_____

_____

With God's love I can...

_____

_____

_____

_____

_____

_____

_____

_____

God loves me despite...

_____

_____

_____

_____

_____

_____

_____

_____

_____

_____

_____

Today I saw God.....

_____

_____

_____

_____

_____

_____

_____

_____

DATE _____

TODAY'S SCRIPTURE READING:

_____
_____
_____

Today I feel God's love through...

_____
_____
_____
_____
_____
_____
_____
_____

Faith means...

_____
_____
_____
_____
_____
_____
_____

A small miracle I have witnessed is...

_____
_____
_____
_____
_____
_____
_____
_____
_____

God, help me today with...

_____
_____
_____
_____
_____
_____
_____

DATE _____   Today I am thankful for...

TODAY'S SCRIPTURE READING:

_____

_____

_____

My prayer to God is...

_____

_____

_____   In my heart today...

_____

_____   _____

_____   _____

_____   _____

_____   _____

My family is a blessing because... _____

_____   _____

_____

_____

_____

_____

_____

_____

_____

_____

DATE _____

TODAY'S SCRIPTURE READING:

_____
_____
_____

I thank God for...

_____
_____
_____
_____
_____
_____
_____
_____
_____

Today I am hoping for...

_____
_____
_____
_____
_____
_____
_____
_____
_____
_____

My life is wonderful today because...

_____
_____
_____
_____
_____
_____
_____
_____

Today I am grateful that God gave me...

_____
_____
_____
_____
_____
_____
_____
_____

DATE _____

TODAY'S SCRIPTURE READING:

_____
_____
_____

I feel God's presence when...

_____
_____
_____
_____
_____
_____
_____
_____

Through God I am working
to forgive...

_____
_____
_____
_____
_____
_____
_____

I need to trust God with...

_____
_____
_____
_____
_____
_____
_____

My faith in God has taught me...

_____
_____
_____
_____
_____
_____
_____
_____

DATE _____

TODAY'S SCRIPTURE READING:

_____
_____
_____

Today I feel blessed because...

_____
_____
_____
_____
_____
_____
_____
_____

I will live God's plan for me by...

_____
_____
_____
_____
_____
_____
_____
_____

Through God I work to better understand people who...

_____
_____
_____
_____
_____
_____
_____
_____

Something that brings me joy is...

_____
_____
_____
_____
_____
_____
_____

DATE _____

TODAY'S SCRIPTURE READING:

_____
_____
_____

Today I ask God for...

_____
_____
_____
_____
_____
_____
_____

I will surrender to God today by...

_____
_____
_____
_____
_____
_____
_____
_____

I am joyful today because...

_____
_____
_____
_____
_____
_____
_____
_____

I feel surrounded by God's love when...

_____
_____
_____
_____
_____
_____
_____

DATE _____

TODAY'S SCRIPTURE READING:

_____
_____
_____

Lord, teach me to...

_____
_____
_____
_____
_____
_____
_____

With God's love I can...

_____
_____
_____
_____
_____
_____
_____
_____
_____
_____

God loves me despite...

_____
_____
_____
_____
_____
_____
_____
_____
_____
_____

Today I saw God.....

_____
_____
_____
_____
_____
_____
_____
_____
_____

DATE _____

TODAY'S SCRIPTURE READING:

_____
_____
_____

Faith means...

_____

Today I feel God's love through...

_____
_____
_____
_____
_____
_____
_____
_____
_____

_____
_____
_____
_____
_____
_____
_____

God, help me today with...

A small miracle I have
witnessed is...

_____
_____
_____
_____
_____
_____

_____
_____
_____
_____
_____
_____
_____
_____

DATE _____

TODAY'S SCRIPTURE READING:

_____
_____
_____
_____

Today I am thankful for...

My prayer to God is...

_____
_____
_____
_____
_____
_____
_____
_____
_____

_____
_____
_____
_____
_____
_____
_____
_____

In my heart today...

My family is a blessing because...

_____
_____
_____
_____
_____
_____
_____
_____
_____

_____
_____
_____
_____
_____
_____
_____
_____
_____

DATE _____

TODAY'S SCRIPTURE READING:

_____
_____
_____

I thank God for...

_____
_____
_____
_____
_____
_____
_____
_____

Today I am hoping for...

_____
_____
_____
_____
_____
_____
_____
_____

My life is wonderful
today because...

_____
_____
_____
_____
_____
_____
_____
_____
_____

Today I am grateful that God
gave me...

_____
_____
_____
_____
_____
_____
_____
_____

DATE _____

TODAY'S SCRIPTURE READING:

_____
_____
_____

I feel God's presence when...

_____
_____
_____
_____
_____
_____
_____
_____

Through God I am working
to forgive...

_____
_____
_____
_____
_____
_____
_____
_____
_____

I need to trust God with...

_____
_____
_____
_____
_____
_____
_____
_____
_____
_____

My faith in God has taught me...

_____
_____
_____
_____
_____
_____
_____
_____
_____

DATE _____

_____
_____
_____

Through God I work to better
understand people who...

Today I feel blessed because...

_____
_____
_____
_____
_____
_____
_____
_____
_____

_____
_____
_____
_____
_____
_____
_____

Something that brings me joy is...

_____
_____

I will live God's plan for me by...

_____
_____
_____
_____
_____
_____
_____

_____
_____
_____
_____
_____
_____
_____
_____

DATE _____

TODAY'S SCRIPTURE READING:

_____
_____
_____

Today I ask God for...

_____
_____
_____
_____
_____
_____
_____
_____

I am joyful today because...

_____
_____
_____
_____
_____

I feel surrounded by God's love when...

_____
_____
_____
_____

I will surrender to God today by...

_____
_____
_____
_____
_____
_____
_____

_____
_____
_____
_____
_____
_____
_____

DATE _____

TODAY'S SCRIPTURE READING:

_____
_____
_____

Lord, teach me to...

_____
_____
_____
_____
_____
_____
_____
_____

With God's love I can...

_____
_____
_____
_____
_____
_____
_____

God loves me despite...

_____
_____
_____
_____
_____
_____
_____
_____
_____
_____
_____

Today I saw God.....

_____
_____
_____
_____
_____
_____
_____

DATE _____

TODAY'S SCRIPTURE READING:

_____
_____
_____

Today I feel God's love through...

_____
_____
_____
_____
_____
_____
_____
_____

Faith means...

_____
_____
_____
_____
_____
_____
_____
_____
_____

A small miracle I have witnessed is...

_____
_____
_____
_____
_____
_____
_____
_____
_____

God, help me today with...

_____
_____
_____
_____
_____
_____
_____
_____

DATE _____   Today I am thankful for...

TODAY'S SCRIPTURE READING:

_____

_____

_____

_____

My prayer to God is...

_____

_____

In my heart today...

_____

_____

_____

_____

_____

My family is a blessing because...

_____

_____

_____

_____

_____

_____

_____

_____

_____

_____

_____

DATE _____

TODAY'S SCRIPTURE READING:

_____
_____
_____

I thank God for...

_____
_____
_____
_____
_____
_____
_____
_____
_____

Today I am hoping for...

_____
_____
_____
_____
_____
_____
_____
_____
_____
_____

My life is wonderful today because...

_____
_____
_____
_____
_____
_____
_____
_____
_____

Today I am grateful that God gave me...

_____
_____
_____
_____
_____
_____
_____
_____
_____

DATE _____

TODAY'S SCRIPTURE READING:

_____
_____
_____

I need to trust God with...

_____
_____
_____
_____
_____
_____
_____
_____

I feel God's presence when...

_____
_____
_____
_____
_____
_____
_____
_____
_____
_____

My faith in God has taught me...

_____
_____
_____
_____
_____

Through God I am working
to forgive...

_____
_____
_____
_____
_____
_____
_____
_____
_____

DATE _____

_____
_____
_____

Today I feel blessed because...

_____
_____
_____
_____
_____
_____
_____
_____
_____

Through God I work to better understand people who...

_____
_____
_____
_____
_____
_____
_____
_____

I will live God's plan for me by...

_____
_____
_____
_____
_____
_____
_____
_____
_____

Something that brings me joy is...

_____
_____
_____
_____
_____
_____
_____
_____

DATE _____   I am joyful today because...

_____   _____
_____   _____
_____   _____
                            _____
Today I ask God for...   _____
                            _____
_____   _____
_____   _____
_____
_____   I feel surrounded by God's
_____   love when...
_____
_____   _____
_____   _____
_____   _____
                            _____
I will surrender to God today by... _____
                            _____
_____   _____
_____   _____
_____   _____
_____
_____
_____
_____
_____
_____

DATE _____

TODAY'S SCRIPTURE READING:

_____
_____
_____

Lord, teach me to...

_____
_____
_____
_____
_____
_____
_____

With God's love I can...

_____
_____
_____
_____
_____
_____
_____
_____
_____

God loves me despite...

_____
_____
_____
_____
_____
_____
_____
_____
_____
_____

Today I saw God.....

_____
_____
_____
_____
_____
_____
_____

DATE _____

TODAY'S SCRIPTURE READING:

_____
_____
_____   Faith means...

Today I feel God's love through...
                                            _____
                                            _____
_____   _____
_____   _____
_____   _____
_____   _____
_____   _____
_____   _____
_____   _____
_____
_____   God, help me today with...
_____
                                            _____
A small miracle I have   _____
witnessed is...   _____
                                            _____
_____   _____
_____   _____
_____   _____
_____   _____
_____   _____
_____   _____
_____   _____

DATE _____

TODAY'S SCRIPTURE READING:

_____
_____
_____

Today I am thankful for...

My prayer to God is...

_____
_____
_____
_____
_____
_____
_____
_____
_____

_____
_____
_____
_____
_____
_____
_____

In my heart today...

My family is a blessing because...

_____
_____
_____
_____
_____
_____
_____
_____

_____
_____
_____
_____
_____
_____
_____
_____

DATE _____

TODAY'S SCRIPTURE READING:

_____
_____
_____

I thank God for...

_____
_____
_____
_____
_____
_____
_____
_____

Today I am hoping for...

_____
_____
_____
_____
_____
_____
_____

My life is wonderful today because...

_____
_____
_____
_____
_____
_____
_____

Today I am grateful that God gave me...

_____
_____
_____
_____
_____
_____

DATE _____

TODAY'S SCRIPTURE READING:

_____
_____
_____

I feel God's presence when...

_____
_____
_____
_____
_____
_____
_____

Through God I am working
to forgive...

_____
_____
_____
_____
_____
_____
_____
_____

I need to trust God with...

_____
_____
_____
_____
_____
_____
_____
_____

My faith in God has taught me...

_____
_____
_____
_____
_____
_____
_____
_____

DATE _____

TODAY'S SCRIPTURE READING:

_____
_____
_____

Through God I work to better understand people who...

_____
_____

Today I feel blessed because...

_____
_____
_____
_____
_____
_____
_____
_____
_____
_____
_____
_____
_____
_____

Something that brings me joy is...

_____
_____
_____
_____
_____

I will live God's plan for me by...

_____
_____
_____
_____
_____
_____
_____
_____
_____
_____
_____
_____

DATE _____

TODAY'S SCRIPTURE READING:

_____
_____
_____

Today I ask God for...

_____
_____
_____
_____
_____
_____
_____
_____

I am joyful today because...

_____
_____
_____
_____
_____

I feel surrounded by God's
love when...

I will surrender to God
today by...

_____
_____
_____
_____
_____
_____
_____

_____
_____
_____
_____
_____
_____
_____

DATE _____

TODAY'S SCRIPTURE READING:

_____
_____
_____

Lord, teach me to...

_____
_____
_____
_____
_____
_____
_____
_____

With God's love I can...

_____
_____
_____
_____
_____
_____
_____

God loves me despite...

_____
_____
_____
_____
_____
_____
_____
_____
_____
_____
_____
_____

Today I saw God.....

_____
_____
_____
_____
_____
_____
_____
_____

DATE _____

TODAY'S SCRIPTURE READING:

_____
_____
_____

Today I feel God's love through...

_____
_____
_____
_____
_____
_____
_____
_____

Faith means...

_____
_____
_____
_____
_____
_____
_____
_____
_____
_____

A small miracle I have witnessed is...

_____
_____
_____
_____
_____
_____
_____
_____
_____

God, help me today with...

_____
_____
_____
_____
_____
_____
_____
_____

DATE _____

TODAY'S SCRIPTURE READING:

_____
_____
_____

My prayer to God is...

_____
_____
_____
_____
_____
_____
_____

My family is a blessing because...

_____
_____
_____
_____
_____
_____
_____
_____

Today I am thankful for...

_____
_____
_____
_____
_____
_____
_____
_____

In my heart today...

_____
_____
_____
_____
_____
_____
_____

DATE _____

TODAY'S SCRIPTURE READING:

_____
_____
_____

I thank God for...

_____
_____
_____
_____
_____
_____
_____

Today I am hoping for...

_____
_____
_____
_____
_____
_____
_____
_____

My life is wonderful today because...

_____
_____
_____
_____
_____
_____
_____
_____

Today I am grateful that God gave me...

_____
_____
_____
_____
_____
_____
_____
_____

DATE _____

TODAY'S SCRIPTURE READING:

_____
_____
_____

I need to trust God with...

I feel God's presence when...

_____
_____
_____
_____
_____
_____
_____
_____
_____

_____
_____
_____
_____
_____
_____
_____

My faith in God has taught me...

_____
_____
Through God I am working
to forgive...

_____
_____
_____
_____
_____
_____
_____

_____
_____
_____
_____
_____
_____

DATE _____

TODAY'S SCRIPTURE READING:

_____
_____
_____

Today I feel blessed because...

_____
_____
_____
_____
_____
_____
_____
_____

Through God I work to better understand people who...

_____
_____
_____
_____
_____
_____
_____
_____

I will live God's plan for me by...

_____
_____
_____
_____
_____
_____
_____
_____

Something that brings me joy is...

_____
_____
_____
_____
_____
_____
_____

DATE _____

TODAY'S SCRIPTURE READING:

_____
_____
_____

Today I ask God for...

_____
_____
_____
_____
_____
_____
_____

I will surrender to God today by...

_____
_____
_____
_____
_____
_____
_____
_____

I am joyful today because...

_____
_____
_____
_____
_____
_____
_____
_____
_____

I feel surrounded by God's
love when...

_____
_____
_____
_____
_____
_____
_____
_____

DATE _____

God loves me despite...

TODAY'S SCRIPTURE READING:

_____

_____

_____

_____

Lord, teach me to...

_____

_____

_____

_____

_____

Today I saw God.....

_____

_____

_____

_____

With God's love I can...

_____

_____

_____

_____

_____

_____

_____

_____

_____

_____

DATE _____

TODAY'S SCRIPTURE READING:

_____
_____
_____

Faith means...

Today I feel God's love through...

_____
_____
_____
_____
_____
_____
_____
_____
_____
_____

God, help me today with...

A small miracle I have
witnessed is...

_____
_____
_____
_____
_____
_____
_____

DATE _____

TODAY'S SCRIPTURE READING:

_____
_____
_____

Today I am thankful for...

_____
_____
_____
_____
_____
_____
_____

My prayer to God is...

_____
_____
_____
_____
_____
_____
_____
_____

In my heart today...

_____
_____

My family is a blessing because...

_____
_____
_____
_____
_____
_____
_____
_____

_____
_____
_____
_____
_____
_____
_____
_____

DATE _____

TODAY'S SCRIPTURE READING:

_____
_____
_____

I thank God for...

_____
_____
_____
_____
_____
_____
_____

Today I am hoping for...

_____
_____
_____
_____
_____
_____
_____

My life is wonderful
today because...

_____
_____
_____
_____
_____
_____
_____

Today I am grateful that God
gave me...

_____
_____
_____
_____
_____
_____

DATE _____

TODAY'S SCRIPTURE READING:

_____
_____
_____

_____
_____
_____
_____
_____
_____
_____
_____

I feel God's presence when...

_____
_____
_____
_____
_____
_____
_____
_____

My faith in God has taught me...

_____
_____
_____
_____
_____
_____

Through God I am working
to forgive...

_____
_____
_____
_____
_____
_____
_____
_____

_____
_____
_____
_____

DATE _____

TODAY'S SCRIPTURE READING:

_____
_____
_____

Through God I work to better
understand people who...

_____

Today I feel blessed because...

_____
_____
_____
_____
_____
_____
_____
_____
_____

_____
_____
_____
_____
_____
_____
_____

Something that brings me joy is...

_____
_____

I will live God's plan for me by...

_____
_____
_____
_____
_____
_____
_____
_____

_____
_____
_____
_____
_____
_____
_____
_____

DATE _____

TODAY'S SCRIPTURE READING:

_____
_____
_____

Today I ask God for...

I am joyful today because...

_____
_____
_____
_____
_____
_____
_____

I feel surrounded by God's love when...

I will surrender to God today by...

_____
_____
_____
_____
_____
_____

_____
_____
_____
_____
_____
_____
_____
_____

DATE _____

TODAY'S SCRIPTURE READING:

_____
_____
_____

Lord, teach me to...

_____
_____
_____
_____
_____
_____
_____

With God's love I can...

_____
_____
_____
_____
_____
_____
_____

God loves me despite...

_____
_____
_____
_____
_____
_____
_____
_____
_____
_____

Today I saw God.....

_____
_____
_____
_____
_____
_____

DATE _____

TODAY'S SCRIPTURE READING:

_____
_____
_____

Today I feel God's love through...

_____
_____
_____
_____
_____
_____
_____
_____

Faith means...

_____
_____
_____
_____
_____
_____
_____
_____

A small miracle I have witnessed is...

_____
_____
_____
_____
_____
_____
_____
_____
_____

God, help me today with...

_____
_____
_____
_____
_____
_____
_____
_____

DATE _____

TODAY'S SCRIPTURE READING:

_____
_____
_____

My prayer to God is...

_____
_____
_____
_____
_____
_____

My family is a blessing because...

_____
_____
_____
_____
_____
_____

Today I am thankful for...

_____
_____
_____
_____
_____
_____
_____

In my heart today...

_____
_____
_____
_____
_____
_____
_____

DATE _____

TODAY'S SCRIPTURE READING:

_____
_____
_____

I thank God for...

_____
_____
_____
_____
_____
_____
_____

Today I am hoping for...

_____
_____
_____
_____
_____
_____
_____
_____

My life is wonderful today because...

_____
_____
_____
_____
_____
_____
_____
_____
_____

Today I am grateful that God gave me...

_____
_____
_____
_____
_____
_____
_____

DATE _____

TODAY'S SCRIPTURE READING:

_____
_____
_____

I need to trust God with...

I feel God's presence when...

_____
_____
_____
_____
_____
_____
_____
_____
_____

My faith in God has taught me...

Through God I am working
to forgive...

_____
_____
_____
_____
_____
_____

DATE _____

TODAY'S SCRIPTURE READING:

_____
_____
_____

Today I feel blessed because...

_____
_____
_____
_____
_____
_____
_____
_____
_____

Through God I work to better understand people who...

_____
_____
_____
_____
_____
_____
_____
_____

I will live God's plan for me by...

_____
_____
_____
_____
_____
_____
_____
_____

Something that brings me joy is...

_____
_____
_____
_____
_____
_____
_____
_____

DATE _____

TODAY'S SCRIPTURE READING:

_____
_____
_____

Today I ask God for...

_____
_____
_____
_____
_____
_____
_____

I will surrender to God today by...

_____
_____
_____
_____
_____
_____
_____
_____

I am joyful today because...

_____
_____
_____
_____
_____
_____
_____

I feel surrounded by God's love when...

_____
_____
_____
_____
_____
_____
_____

DATE _____

TODAY'S SCRIPTURE READING:

_____
_____
_____

Lord, teach me to...

_____
_____
_____
_____
_____
_____

With God's love I can...

_____
_____
_____
_____
_____
_____
_____
_____

God loves me despite...

_____
_____
_____
_____
_____
_____
_____

Today I saw God.....

_____
_____
_____
_____
_____
_____
_____
_____

DATE _____

TODAY'S SCRIPTURE READING:

_____
_____
_____

Faith means...

Today I feel God's love through...

_____
_____
_____
_____
_____
_____
_____

God, help me today with...

A small miracle I have
witnessed is...

_____
_____
_____
_____
_____

DATE _____

TODAY'S SCRIPTURE READING:

_____
_____
_____

Today I am thankful for...

My prayer to God is...

_____
_____
_____
_____
_____
_____
_____
_____
_____

_____
_____
_____
_____
_____
_____
_____

In my heart today...

My family is a blessing because...

_____
_____
_____
_____
_____
_____
_____
_____
_____

_____
_____
_____
_____
_____
_____
_____
_____

DATE _____

TODAY'S SCRIPTURE READING:

_____
_____
_____

I thank God for...

_____
_____
_____
_____
_____
_____
_____

Today I am hoping for...

_____
_____
_____
_____
_____
_____
_____
_____

My life is wonderful
today because...

_____
_____
_____
_____
_____
_____
_____
_____

Today I am grateful that God
gave me...

_____
_____
_____
_____
_____

DATE _____

TODAY'S SCRIPTURE READING:

_____
_____
_____

I feel God's presence when...

_____
_____
_____
_____
_____
_____
_____
_____

Through God I am working
to forgive...

_____
_____
_____
_____
_____
_____
_____
_____
_____

I need to trust God with...

_____
_____
_____
_____
_____
_____
_____
_____
_____
_____

My faith in God has taught me...

_____
_____
_____
_____
_____
_____

DATE _____

TODAY'S SCRIPTURE READING:

_____
_____
_____

Through God I work to better understand people who...

_____
_____

Today I feel blessed because...

_____
_____
_____
_____
_____
_____
_____
_____
_____
_____

_____
_____
_____
_____
_____
_____
_____

Something that brings me joy is...

_____
_____
_____

I will live God's plan for me by...

_____
_____
_____
_____
_____
_____
_____
_____

_____
_____
_____
_____
_____
_____
_____
_____
_____
_____

DATE _____

TODAY'S SCRIPTURE READING:

_____
_____
_____

Today I ask God for...

_____
_____
_____
_____
_____
_____
_____
_____
_____

I will surrender to God
today by...

_____
_____
_____
_____
_____
_____
_____

I am joyful today because...

_____
_____
_____
_____
_____

I feel surrounded by God's
love when...

_____
_____
_____
_____
_____
_____
_____
_____
_____

DATE _____   God loves me despite...

TODAY'S SCRIPTURE READING: _____
                                   _____
_____   _____
_____   _____
_____   _____
                                   _____
                                   _____
Lord, teach me to...   _____
                                   _____
_____   _____
_____   _____
_____
_____   Today I saw God.....
_____
_____   _____
_____   _____
_____   _____
                                   _____
                                   _____
With God's love I can...   _____

_____
_____
_____
_____
_____
_____
_____

DATE _____

TODAY'S SCRIPTURE READING:

_____
_____
_____

Today I feel God's love through...

Faith means...

_____
_____
_____
_____
_____
_____
_____
_____

_____
_____
_____
_____
_____
_____
_____
_____
_____

A small miracle I have witnessed is...

_____
_____
_____
_____
_____
_____
_____
_____

God, help me today with...

_____
_____
_____
_____
_____
_____
_____

DATE _____   Today I am thankful for...

TODAY'S SCRIPTURE READING: _____
                               _____
_____   _____
_____   _____
_____   _____
                               _____
                               _____
My prayer to God is...   _____
                               _____
_____
_____   In my heart today...
_____
_____   _____
_____   _____
_____   _____
_____   _____
_____   _____
                               _____
My family is a blessing because... _____
                               _____
_____   _____
_____   _____
_____
_____
_____
_____
_____
_____
_____
_____

DATE _____

_____
_____
_____

I thank God for...

_____
_____
_____
_____
_____
_____
_____

Today I am hoping for...

_____
_____
_____
_____
_____
_____
_____
_____
_____

My life is wonderful today because...

_____
_____
_____
_____
_____
_____
_____
_____
_____

Today I am grateful that God gave me...

_____
_____
_____
_____
_____
_____
_____
_____
_____

DATE _____

TODAY'S SCRIPTURE READING:

_____
_____
_____

I need to trust God with...

I feel God's presence when...

_____
_____
_____
_____
_____
_____
_____
_____
_____

_____
_____
_____
_____
_____
_____
_____

My faith in God has taught me...

_____
_____

Through God I am working
to forgive...

_____
_____
_____
_____
_____
_____
_____
_____

_____
_____
_____
_____
_____
_____
_____
_____

DATE _____

TODAY'S SCRIPTURE READING:

_____
_____
_____

Today I feel blessed because...

_____
_____
_____
_____
_____
_____
_____
_____

I will live God's plan for me by...

_____
_____
_____
_____
_____
_____
_____
_____

Through God I work to better
understand people who...

_____
_____
_____
_____
_____
_____
_____
_____

Something that brings me joy is...

_____
_____
_____
_____
_____
_____
_____

DATE _____

TODAY'S SCRIPTURE READING:

_____
_____
_____

Today I ask God for...

_____
_____
_____
_____
_____
_____
_____
_____

I will surrender to God today by...

_____
_____
_____
_____
_____
_____
_____
_____
_____

I am joyful today because...

_____
_____
_____
_____
_____
_____
_____
_____

I feel surrounded by God's
love when...

_____
_____
_____
_____
_____
_____
_____
_____
_____

DATE _____

God loves me despite...

TODAY'S SCRIPTURE READING:

_____
_____
_____
_____
_____
_____
_____
_____

Lord, teach me to...

_____
_____
_____
_____
_____

Today I saw God.....

_____
_____
_____
_____
_____

With God's love I can...

_____
_____
_____
_____
_____
_____
_____
_____
_____

DATE _____

TODAY'S SCRIPTURE READING:

_____
_____
_____

Faith means...

Today I feel God's love through...

_____
_____
_____
_____
_____
_____
_____
_____
_____

God, help me today with...

A small miracle I have
witnessed is...

_____
_____
_____
_____
_____

DATE _____

TODAY'S SCRIPTURE READING:

_____
_____
_____

Today I am thankful for...

My prayer to God is...

_____
_____
_____
_____
_____
_____
_____
_____
_____

_____
_____
_____
_____
_____
_____
_____

In my heart today...

My family is a blessing because...

_____
_____
_____
_____
_____
_____
_____
_____
_____

_____
_____
_____
_____
_____
_____
_____
_____
_____

DATE _____

TODAY'S SCRIPTURE READING:

_____
_____
_____

I thank God for...

_____
_____
_____
_____
_____
_____
_____
_____

Today I am hoping for...

_____
_____
_____
_____
_____
_____
_____

My life is wonderful
today because...

_____
_____
_____
_____
_____
_____
_____

Today I am grateful that God
gave me...

_____
_____
_____
_____
_____
_____

DATE _____

TODAY'S SCRIPTURE READING:

_____
_____
_____

I feel God's presence when...

_____
_____
_____
_____
_____
_____
_____

Through God I am working
to forgive...

_____
_____
_____
_____
_____
_____
_____
_____
_____

I need to trust God with...

_____
_____
_____
_____
_____
_____
_____
_____

My faith in God has taught me...

_____
_____
_____
_____
_____
_____
_____
_____

DATE _____

TODAY'S SCRIPTURE READING:

_____

_____

_____

Through God I work to better
understand people who...

_____

_____

_____

_____

_____

_____

_____

_____

Today I feel blessed because...

_____

_____

_____

_____

_____

_____

_____

_____

_____

Something that brings me joy is...

_____

_____

_____

_____

I will live God's plan for me by...

_____

_____

_____

_____

_____

_____

_____

_____

_____

_____

_____

_____

_____

_____

_____

DATE _____

TODAY'S SCRIPTURE READING:

_____
_____
_____

Today I ask God for...

_____
_____
_____
_____
_____
_____
_____
_____

I am joyful today because...

_____
_____
_____
_____

I feel surrounded by God's
love when...

_____

I will surrender to God
today by...

_____
_____
_____
_____
_____
_____

_____
_____
_____
_____
_____
_____
_____

DATE _____

TODAY'S SCRIPTURE READING:

_____
_____
_____

Lord, teach me to...

_____
_____
_____
_____
_____
_____
_____

With God's love I can...

_____
_____
_____
_____
_____
_____
_____

God loves me despite...

_____
_____
_____
_____
_____
_____
_____
_____
_____

Today I saw God.....

_____
_____
_____
_____
_____
_____
_____

DATE _____

TODAY'S SCRIPTURE READING:

_____
_____
_____

Today I feel God's love through...

_____
_____
_____
_____
_____
_____
_____
_____

Faith means...

_____
_____
_____
_____
_____
_____
_____
_____

A small miracle I have witnessed is...

_____
_____
_____
_____
_____
_____
_____
_____
_____

God, help me today with...

_____
_____
_____
_____
_____
_____
_____

DATE _____

TODAY'S SCRIPTURE READING:

_____
_____
_____

My prayer to God is...

_____
_____
_____
_____
_____
_____
_____
_____

My family is a blessing because...

_____
_____
_____
_____
_____
_____
_____
_____

Today I am thankful for...

_____
_____
_____
_____
_____
_____
_____
_____

In my heart today...

_____
_____
_____
_____
_____
_____
_____
_____

DATE _____

My life is wonderful today because...

TODAY'S SCRIPTURE READING:

_____

_____

_____

_____

_____

I thank God for...

_____

_____

_____

Today I am grateful that God gave me...

_____

_____

_____

_____

Today I am hoping for...

_____

DATE _____

TODAY'S SCRIPTURE READING:

_____
_____
_____

I feel God's presence when...

_____
_____
_____
_____
_____
_____
_____
_____

Through God I am working
to forgive...

_____
_____
_____
_____
_____
_____

I need to trust God with...

_____
_____
_____
_____
_____
_____
_____

My faith in God has taught me...

_____
_____
_____
_____
_____
_____
_____
_____
_____
_____

DATE _____

TODAY'S SCRIPTURE READING:

_____
_____
_____

Today I feel blessed because...

_____
_____
_____
_____
_____
_____
_____
_____

I will live God's plan for me by...

_____
_____
_____
_____
_____
_____
_____
_____

Through God I work to better understand people who...

_____
_____
_____
_____
_____
_____
_____
_____

Something that brings me joy is...

_____
_____
_____
_____
_____
_____
_____

DATE _____

TODAY'S SCRIPTURE READING:

_____
_____
_____

Today I ask God for...

_____
_____
_____
_____
_____
_____
_____
_____

I will surrender to God today by...

_____
_____
_____
_____
_____
_____
_____
_____

I am joyful today because...

_____
_____
_____
_____
_____
_____
_____
_____

I feel surrounded by God's
love when...

_____
_____
_____
_____
_____
_____
_____

DATE _____

God loves me despite...

TODAY'S SCRIPTURE READING:

_____
_____
_____

_____
_____
_____
_____
_____
_____
_____
_____

Lord, teach me to...

_____
_____
_____
_____
_____
_____
_____
_____

Today I saw God.....

_____
_____
_____
_____

With God's love I can...

_____
_____
_____
_____
_____
_____
_____
_____
_____
_____

_____
_____
_____
_____

DATE _____

TODAY'S SCRIPTURE READING:

_____
_____
_____

Faith means...

Today I feel God's love through...

_____
_____
_____
_____
_____
_____
_____
_____
_____
_____
_____
_____

God, help me today with...

A small miracle I have
witnessed is...

_____
_____
_____
_____
_____
_____
_____

DATE _____

TODAY'S SCRIPTURE READING:

_____

_____

_____

Today I am thankful for...

My prayer to God is...

_____

_____

_____

_____

_____

_____

_____

_____

_____

_____

_____

_____

_____

_____

_____

_____

_____

_____

In my heart today...

My family is a blessing because...

_____

_____

_____

_____

_____

_____

_____

_____

_____

_____

_____

_____

_____

_____

_____

_____

_____

DATE _____

My life is wonderful
today because...

_____

_____

_____

I thank God for...

_____

_____

_____

_____

_____

_____

_____

Today I am grateful that God
gave me...

_____

_____

_____

_____

_____

Today I am hoping for...

_____

_____

_____

_____

_____

_____

_____

DATE _____

_____
_____
_____

I feel God's presence when...

_____
_____
_____
_____
_____
_____
_____

Through God I am working
to forgive...

_____
_____
_____
_____
_____
_____
_____
_____

I need to trust God with...

_____
_____
_____
_____
_____
_____
_____
_____
_____
_____

My faith in God has taught me...

_____
_____
_____
_____
_____
_____
_____
_____
_____

DATE _____

TODAY'S SCRIPTURE READING:

_____
_____
_____

Through God I work to better
understand people who...

Today I feel blessed because...

_____
_____
_____
_____
_____
_____
_____
_____
_____

I will live God's plan for me by...

_____
_____
_____
_____
_____
_____
_____

_____
_____
_____
_____
_____
_____
_____
_____

Something that brings me joy is...

_____
_____
_____
_____
_____
_____
_____
_____
_____
_____

DATE _____

TODAY'S SCRIPTURE READING:

_____
_____
_____

Today I ask God for...

_____
_____
_____
_____
_____
_____
_____
_____

I will surrender to God
today by...

_____
_____
_____
_____
_____
_____

I am joyful today because...

_____
_____
_____
_____
_____

I feel surrounded by God's
love when...

_____
_____
_____
_____
_____
_____
_____
_____

DATE _____

TODAY'S SCRIPTURE READING:

_____
_____
_____

Lord, teach me to...

_____
_____
_____
_____
_____
_____
_____

With God's love I can...

_____
_____
_____
_____
_____
_____
_____

An imperfection that God loves me for is...

_____
_____
_____
_____
_____
_____
_____
_____
_____

Today I saw God.....

_____
_____
_____
_____
_____
_____
_____

DATE _____

TODAY'S SCRIPTURE READING:

_____
_____
_____

Today I feel God's love through...

_____
_____
_____
_____
_____
_____
_____
_____
_____

Faith means...

_____
_____
_____
_____
_____
_____
_____
_____
_____

A small miracle I have witnessed is...

_____
_____
_____
_____
_____
_____
_____
_____
_____

God, help me today with...

_____
_____
_____
_____
_____
_____
_____
_____

DATE _____

TODAY'S SCRIPTURE READING:

_____
_____
_____

My prayer to God is...

_____
_____
_____
_____
_____
_____
_____

My family is a blessing because...

_____
_____
_____
_____
_____
_____
_____
_____
_____

Today I am thankful for...

_____
_____
_____
_____
_____
_____
_____
_____
_____

In my heart today...

_____
_____
_____
_____
_____
_____
_____
_____

DATE _____

TODAY'S SCRIPTURE READING:

_____
_____
_____

I thank God for...

_____
_____
_____
_____
_____
_____
_____

Today I am hoping for...

_____
_____
_____
_____
_____
_____
_____
_____

My life is wonderful today because...

_____
_____
_____
_____
_____
_____
_____

Today I am grateful that God gave me...

_____
_____
_____
_____
_____
_____
_____
_____
_____

DATE

TODAY'S SCRIPTURE READING:

_____
_____
_____

I feel God's presence when...

_____
_____
_____
_____
_____
_____
_____
_____
_____

Through God I am working
to forgive...

_____
_____
_____
_____
_____
_____

I need to trust God with...

_____
_____
_____
_____
_____
_____
_____

My faith in God has taught me...

_____
_____
_____
_____
_____
_____
_____
_____
_____

DATE _____

TODAY'S SCRIPTURE READING:

_____
_____
_____

Today I feel blessed because...

_____
_____
_____
_____
_____
_____
_____
_____
_____

Through God I work to better understand people who...

_____
_____
_____
_____
_____
_____
_____
_____

I will live God's plan for me by...

_____
_____
_____
_____
_____
_____
_____
_____
_____

Something that brings me joy is...

_____
_____
_____
_____
_____
_____
_____
_____

DATE _____

TODAY'S SCRIPTURE READING:

_____
_____
_____

Today I ask God for...

_____
_____
_____
_____
_____
_____

I will surrender to God today by...

_____
_____
_____
_____
_____
_____
_____

I am joyful today because...

_____
_____
_____
_____
_____
_____
_____
_____

I feel surrounded by God's
love when...

_____
_____
_____
_____
_____
_____
_____

DATE _____

TODAY'S SCRIPTURE READING:

_____
_____
_____

Lord, teach me to...

_____
_____
_____
_____
_____
_____
_____

With God's love I can...

_____
_____
_____
_____
_____
_____
_____
_____
_____

God loves me despite...

_____
_____
_____
_____
_____
_____
_____
_____

Today I saw God.....

_____
_____
_____
_____
_____
_____
_____

DATE _____

TODAY'S SCRIPTURE READING:

_____
_____
_____

Faith means...

Today I feel God's love through...

_____
_____
_____
_____
_____
_____
_____
_____
_____

_____
_____
_____
_____
_____
_____
_____
_____

God, help me today with...

A small miracle I have
witnessed is...

_____
_____
_____
_____
_____
_____
_____
_____

_____
_____
_____
_____
_____
_____
_____
_____
_____

DATE _____

TODAY'S SCRIPTURE READING:

_____

_____

_____

Today I am thankful for...

My prayer to God is...

_____

_____

_____

_____

_____

_____

_____

_____

_____

_____

_____

In my heart today...

My family is a blessing because...

_____

_____

_____

_____

_____

_____

_____

_____

_____

_____

DATE _____

TODAY'S SCRIPTURE READING:

_____
_____
_____

I thank God for...

_____
_____
_____
_____
_____
_____
_____
_____

Today I am hoping for...

_____
_____
_____
_____
_____
_____
_____
_____

My life is wonderful
today because...

_____
_____
_____
_____
_____
_____
_____
_____
_____

Today I am grateful that God
gave me...

_____
_____
_____
_____
_____
_____
_____
_____

DATE _____

TODAY'S SCRIPTURE READING:

_____
_____
_____

I feel God's presence when...

_____
_____
_____
_____
_____
_____
_____

Through God I am working
to forgive...

_____
_____
_____
_____
_____
_____
_____
_____
_____

I need to trust God with...

_____
_____
_____
_____
_____
_____
_____
_____
_____
_____

My faith in God has taught me...

_____
_____
_____
_____
_____
_____
_____
_____
_____

DATE _____

TODAY'S SCRIPTURE READING:

_____
_____
_____

Through God I work to better
understand people who...

_____
_____
_____
_____
_____
_____
_____
_____

Today I feel blessed because...

_____
_____
_____
_____
_____
_____
_____
_____
_____

Something that brings me joy is...

_____
_____
_____
_____
_____

I will live God's plan for me by...

_____
_____
_____
_____
_____
_____
_____
_____
_____
_____
_____
_____
_____

DATE _____

TODAY'S SCRIPTURE READING:

_____
_____
_____

Today I ask God for...

_____
_____
_____
_____
_____
_____
_____
_____
_____

I will surrender to God
today by...

_____
_____
_____
_____
_____
_____

I am joyful today because...

_____
_____
_____
_____

I feel surrounded by God's
love when...

_____
_____
_____
_____
_____
_____
_____
_____

DATE _____

TODAY'S SCRIPTURE READING:

_____
_____
_____

Lord, teach me to...

_____
_____
_____
_____
_____
_____
_____
_____

With God's love I can...

_____
_____
_____
_____
_____
_____
_____
_____
_____

God loves me despite...

_____
_____
_____
_____
_____
_____
_____
_____
_____
_____

Today I saw God.....

_____
_____
_____
_____
_____
_____
_____

DATE _____

_____
_____
_____

Today I feel God's love through...

_____
_____
_____
_____
_____
_____
_____
_____

Faith means...

_____
_____
_____
_____
_____
_____

A small miracle I have witnessed is...

_____
_____

God, help me today with...

_____
_____
_____
_____
_____
_____
_____
_____
_____

DATE _____

TODAY'S SCRIPTURE READING:

_____
_____
_____

My prayer to God is...

_____
_____
_____
_____
_____
_____
_____

My family is a blessing because...

_____
_____
_____
_____
_____
_____
_____
_____
_____

Today I am thankful for...

_____
_____
_____
_____
_____
_____
_____

In my heart today...

_____
_____
_____
_____
_____
_____
_____
_____

DATE _____

My life is wonderful today because...

TODAY'S SCRIPTURE READING:

_____

_____

_____

_____

_____

I thank God for...

_____

_____

_____

_____

_____

_____

Today I am grateful that God
gave me...

_____

_____

_____

_____

_____

_____

Today I am hoping for...

_____

_____

_____

_____

_____

_____

_____

_____

_____

DATE _____

TODAY'S SCRIPTURE READING:

_____
_____
_____

I need to trust God with...

I feel God's presence when...

_____
_____
_____
_____
_____
_____
_____
_____
_____
_____

_____
_____
_____
_____
_____
_____

My faith in God has taught me...

Through God I am working
to forgive...

_____
_____
_____
_____
_____
_____

_____
_____
_____
_____
_____
_____
_____
_____

DATE _____

_____
_____
_____

Today I feel blessed because...

_____
_____
_____
_____
_____
_____
_____
_____
_____

Through God I work to better understand people who...

_____
_____
_____
_____
_____
_____
_____
_____
_____

I will live God's plan for me by...

_____
_____
_____
_____
_____
_____
_____
_____

Something that brings me joy is...

_____
_____
_____
_____
_____
_____

DATE _____   I am joyful today because...

_____

_____

_____

Today I ask God for...

_____

_____

_____   I feel surrounded by God's
                            love when...
_____

_____   _____

_____   _____

_____   _____

_____   _____

I will surrender to God today by...   _____

_____   _____

_____   _____

_____   _____

_____

_____

_____

_____

_____

DATE _____

TODAY'S SCRIPTURE READING:

_____
_____
_____

Lord, teach me to...

_____
_____
_____
_____
_____
_____
_____
_____

With God's love I can...

_____
_____
_____
_____
_____
_____
_____
_____

God loves me despite...

_____
_____
_____
_____
_____
_____
_____
_____
_____

Today I saw God.....

_____
_____
_____
_____
_____
_____
_____
_____

DATE _____

TODAY'S SCRIPTURE READING:

_____
_____
_____

Faith means...

_____

Today I feel God's love through...

_____
_____
_____
_____
_____
_____
_____
_____
_____
_____

God, help me today with...

A small miracle I have
witnessed is...

_____
_____
_____
_____
_____
_____
_____
_____
_____
_____

DATE _____

TODAY'S SCRIPTURE READING:

_____
_____
_____

Today I am thankful for...

My prayer to God is...

_____
_____
_____
_____
_____
_____
_____
_____

_____
_____
_____
_____
_____
_____
_____

In my heart today...

My family is a blessing because...

_____
_____
_____
_____
_____
_____
_____
_____
_____

_____
_____
_____
_____
_____
_____
_____
_____

DATE _____

TODAY'S SCRIPTURE READING:

_____
_____
_____

I thank God for...

_____
_____
_____
_____
_____
_____
_____

Today I am hoping for...

_____
_____
_____
_____
_____
_____
_____
_____

My life is wonderful
today because...

_____
_____
_____
_____
_____
_____
_____

Today I am grateful that God
gave me...

_____
_____
_____
_____
_____
_____
_____

DATE _____

TODAY'S SCRIPTURE READING:

_____
_____
_____

I feel God's presence when...

_____
_____
_____
_____
_____
_____

Through God I am working
to forgive...

_____
_____
_____
_____
_____
_____
_____
_____

I need to trust God with...

_____
_____
_____
_____
_____
_____
_____
_____

My faith in God has taught me...

_____
_____
_____
_____
_____
_____
_____
_____
_____

DATE _____

TODAY'S SCRIPTURE READING:

_____
_____
_____

Through God I work to better understand people who...

Today I feel blessed because...

_____
_____
_____
_____
_____
_____
_____
_____
_____
_____
_____

_____
_____
_____
_____
_____
_____
_____

Something that brings me joy is...

I will live God's plan for me by...

_____
_____
_____
_____
_____
_____
_____
_____

_____
_____
_____
_____
_____
_____
_____
_____

DATE _____

TODAY'S SCRIPTURE READING:

_____
_____
_____

Today I ask God for...

_____
_____
_____
_____
_____
_____
_____
_____

I am joyful today because...

_____
_____
_____
_____
_____

I feel surrounded by God's love when...

_____
_____
_____
_____
_____

I will surrender to God today by...

_____
_____
_____
_____
_____
_____

_____
_____
_____
_____

DATE _____

God loves me despite...

_____

_____

_____

_____

_____

_____

Lord, teach me to...

_____

_____

_____

_____

_____

_____

_____

Today I saw God.....

_____

_____

_____

_____

_____

_____

With God's love I can...

_____

_____

_____

_____

_____

_____

_____

DATE _____

TODAY'S SCRIPTURE READING:

_____
_____
_____

Today I feel God's love through...

_____
_____
_____
_____
_____
_____
_____
_____
_____

Faith means...

_____
_____
_____
_____
_____
_____
_____
_____

A small miracle I have witnessed is...

_____
_____
_____
_____
_____
_____
_____
_____

God, help me today with...

_____
_____
_____
_____
_____
_____
_____
_____

DATE _____ Today I am thankful for...

TODAY'S SCRIPTURE READING:

_____

_____

_____

_____

My prayer to God is...

_____

_____

_____

_____

_____

_____

In my heart today...

_____

_____

_____

_____

_____

_____

My family is a blessing because...

_____

_____

_____

_____

_____

_____

_____

_____

_____

_____

DATE _____

TODAY'S SCRIPTURE READING:

_____
_____
_____

I thank God for...

_____
_____
_____
_____
_____
_____
_____

Today I am hoping for...

_____
_____
_____
_____
_____
_____
_____
_____
_____

My life is wonderful today because...

_____
_____
_____
_____
_____
_____
_____
_____

Today I am grateful that God gave me...

_____
_____
_____
_____
_____
_____
_____
_____

DATE _____

TODAY'S SCRIPTURE READING:

_____
_____
_____

I feel God's presence when...

_____
_____
_____
_____
_____
_____
_____
_____
_____

Through God I am working
to forgive...

_____
_____
_____
_____
_____
_____

I need to trust God with...

_____
_____
_____
_____
_____
_____
_____

My faith in God has taught me...

_____
_____
_____
_____
_____
_____
_____
_____
_____

DATE _____

TODAY'S SCRIPTURE READING:

_____
_____
_____

Today I feel blessed because...

_____
_____
_____
_____
_____
_____
_____
_____

Through God I work to better understand people who...

_____
_____
_____
_____
_____
_____
_____
_____

I will live God's plan for me by...

_____
_____
_____
_____
_____
_____
_____
_____

Something that brings me joy is...

_____
_____
_____
_____
_____
_____

DATE _____

TODAY'S SCRIPTURE READING:

_____

_____

_____

Today I ask God for...

_____

_____

_____

_____

_____

_____

_____

I will surrender to God today by...

_____

_____

_____

_____

_____

_____

_____

_____

I am joyful today because...

_____

_____

_____

_____

_____

_____

_____

_____

I feel surrounded by God's love when...

_____

_____

_____

_____

_____

_____

_____

_____

DATE _____

TODAY'S SCRIPTURE READING:

_____
_____
_____

_____
_____
_____
_____
_____
_____
_____

Lord, teach me to...

_____
_____
_____
_____
_____
_____
_____

Today I saw God.....

_____
_____
_____
_____
_____

With God's love I can...

_____
_____
_____
_____
_____
_____
_____
_____
_____
_____

DATE _____

TODAY'S SCRIPTURE READING:

_____
_____
_____

Faith means...

Today I feel God's love through...

_____
_____
_____
_____
_____
_____
_____
_____
_____
_____

_____
_____
_____
_____
_____
_____
_____
_____

God, help me today with...

A small miracle I have
witnessed is...

_____
_____
_____
_____
_____
_____

_____
_____
_____
_____
_____
_____
_____
_____

DATE _____

TODAY'S SCRIPTURE READING:

_____
_____
_____

Today I am thankful for...

My prayer to God is...

_____
_____
_____
_____
_____
_____
_____
_____
_____

_____
_____
_____
_____
_____
_____
_____
_____

In my heart today...

My family is a blessing because...

_____
_____
_____
_____
_____
_____
_____
_____
_____

_____
_____
_____
_____
_____
_____
_____
_____

DATE _____

TODAY'S SCRIPTURE READING:

_____
_____
_____

I thank God for...

_____
_____
_____
_____
_____
_____
_____

Today I am hoping for...

_____
_____
_____
_____
_____
_____
_____

My life is wonderful
today because...

_____
_____
_____
_____
_____
_____
_____
_____

Today I am grateful that God
gave me...

_____
_____
_____
_____
_____
_____

DATE _____

TODAY'S SCRIPTURE READING:

_____

_____

_____

I feel God's presence when...

_____

_____

_____

_____

_____

_____

_____

Through God I am working
to forgive...

_____

_____

_____

_____

_____

_____

_____

_____

I need to trust God with...

_____

_____

_____

_____

_____

_____

_____

_____

_____

My faith in God has taught me...

_____

_____

_____

_____

_____

_____

_____

_____

_____

DATE _____

TODAY'S SCRIPTURE READING:

_____
_____
_____

Through God I work to better understand people who...

Today I feel blessed because...

_____
_____
_____
_____
_____
_____
_____
_____
_____

_____
_____
_____
_____
_____
_____
_____

Something that brings me joy is...

I will live God's plan for me by...

_____
_____
_____
_____
_____
_____
_____
_____

_____
_____
_____
_____
_____
_____
_____
_____

DATE _____

TODAY'S SCRIPTURE READING:

_____
_____
_____

Today I ask God for...

I am joyful today because...

_____
_____
_____
_____
_____
_____
_____
_____
_____

I feel surrounded by God's love when...

I will surrender to God today by...

_____
_____
_____
_____
_____
_____

DATE _____

God loves me despite...

TODAY'S SCRIPTURE READING:

_____
_____
_____

_____
_____
_____
_____
_____
_____
_____

Lord, teach me to...

_____
_____
_____
_____
_____
_____
_____

_____
_____
_____

Today I saw God.....

_____
_____
_____
_____
_____
_____

With God's love I can...

_____
_____
_____
_____
_____
_____
_____
_____

DATE _____

TODAY'S SCRIPTURE READING:

_____
_____
_____

Today I feel God's love through...

Faith means...

_____
_____
_____
_____
_____
_____
_____
_____

A small miracle I have witnessed is...

_____
_____
_____
_____
_____
_____
_____
_____

God, help me today with...

_____
_____
_____
_____
_____
_____

DATE _____

Today I am thankful for...

TODAY'S SCRIPTURE READING:

_____

_____

_____

_____

_____

_____

_____

_____

My prayer to God is...

_____

_____

In my heart today...

_____

_____

_____

_____

_____

_____

_____

_____

_____

_____

_____

My family is a blessing because...

_____

_____

_____

_____

_____

_____

_____

_____

_____

_____

DATE _____

My life is wonderful today because...

_____
_____
_____
_____
_____
_____
_____

TODAY'S SCRIPTURE READING:

_____
_____
_____

I thank God for...

_____
_____
_____
_____

Today I am grateful that God gave me...

_____
_____
_____
_____
_____
_____
_____
_____

Today I am hoping for...

_____
_____
_____
_____
_____
_____
_____
_____
_____

DATE _____

TODAY'S SCRIPTURE READING:

_____
_____
_____

I feel God's presence when...

_____
_____
_____
_____
_____
_____
_____
_____

Through God I am working
to forgive...

_____
_____
_____
_____
_____
_____
_____

I need to trust God with...

_____
_____
_____
_____
_____
_____
_____

My faith in God has taught me...

_____
_____
_____
_____
_____
_____
_____
_____

DATE _____

TODAY'S SCRIPTURE READING:

_____
_____
_____

Today I feel blessed because...

_____
_____
_____
_____
_____
_____
_____
_____

Through God I work to better understand people who...

_____
_____
_____
_____
_____
_____
_____

I will live God's plan for me by...

_____
_____
_____
_____
_____
_____
_____
_____

Something that brings me joy is...

_____
_____
_____
_____
_____
_____
_____